I Believe in Santa!

Illustrated by Gill Guile

Story by Deborah Campbell-Todd

It was Christmas Eve and it was time for bed.
"Bed now, Tom and Molly," said Mum.
"Otherwise Santa won't visit in the night and you'll have no presents!"
"I'm a big boy, now," said Tom. "I don't believe in Santa!"

"Oh, dear," said Mum. "Don't let Santa hear you say that!
Of course there's a Santa."
"Yes there is!" said Molly. "Who brings all the snow and the presents?"
Mum tucked Tom and Molly into bed. "Sleep now," she said.

2

Tom and Molly were excited and tired and they were soon asleep.
Outside it was very cold and the moon shone brightly on the snow in
the garden. It looked like a white blanket.

Tom was dreaming about toy cars and footballs. And he could hear bells ringing. The noise woke him up – and he could still hear bells ringing! "Wake up, Molly," he whispered. "Can you hear that noise?"

"It's bells!" she said. "And it's coming from the garden."

Molly and Tom ran to the window, and they both looked out.
What a sight met their eyes!
They saw Santa. He was dressed in red, with a fluffy white beard.
He was huffing and puffing and putting presents on his sleigh.

"Ooh!" squealed Molly. "Look!"
Santa must have heard Molly because he quickly turned round and looked up at their window. He put his arms out wide, trying to hide the sleigh behind him, but it was far too big for that!

Tom quickly opened the window.
"What's wrong?" he called out.
"Oh dear, oh dear!" Santa said. "You're not supposed to see me!
Look the other way while I put all these presents back on the sleigh."

Santa tried to put all the presents back on the sleigh, but they were such difficult shapes, they wouldn't all go on. They kept falling off!
Tom and Molly looked at each other.
"Let's go!" said Tom, and they quickly and quietly ran downstairs.

A moment later they were outside, wearing boots, gloves and thick coats.
"We'll help," said Molly.
"Children want such different toys nowadays," sighed Santa.
"It makes my life very difficult."

"Skate boards and scooters are so awkward to pack," said Santa,
squeezing a strange shaped parcel on to the sleigh only for
another one to fall off. Tom clambered onto the sleigh.
"If I hold on to these, you can get some more on."

"It's no good," said Santa after a few minutes.
"There's only one thing for it – you two will have to come with me
and help me deliver all these!"
"Yes, please!" cried Tom and Molly.
"Jump on, then" said Santa, and then he called, "Come away, my reindeer!"

The reindeer leapt into the air, pulling the sleigh behind them.
Tom and Molly held tightly to the parcels and Santa
drove off into the night sky.
What a journey! They flew through the cold night air
and looked down on all the houses.

Santa stopped at every house, and taking parcels from the sleigh,
he magically disappeared down each chimney to deliver
them to the children. The pile of parcels in the back of the sleigh
went down and Molly and Tom didn't have to hold on to the
parcels any more. They soon fell asleep under the warm blanket.

Santa finished delivering the parcels and arrived back at
Molly and Tom's house. "Wake up, sleepy heads!" he said.
"Thank you for all your help!"
"Are we finished?" asked Molly, yawning.
"For this year," said Santa. "There's always next year!"

"Can we do it again next year?" asked Tom.
"Then you do believe in me?" asked Santa with a smile.
"Oh, yes!" said Tom.
"Thank you so much for taking us."
"Back to bed now," said Santa. Merry Christmas!
Goodbye until next year!"

"Merry Christmas!" said Mum, as she woke Molly and Tom.
Molly and Tom ran downstairs to find parcels under the tree.
Santa had delivered their presents, too. A little note said, "Thank you!"
"I can't wait until next year," Molly said to Tom.